Fighting the Mill Creeks

Being a Personal Account of Campaigns
Against Indians of the Northern
Sierras

Chico, California
The Chico Record Press
1909

FIGHTING THE MILL CREEKS

CHAPTER I.

CROSSING the plains in '57, I tried mining for a short time on the North Fork of Feather River, but soon continued my journey to the Sacramento Valley and settled on Deer Creek. With broad plains to the north and south fit only for grazing purposes, the fertile land along the creek bottom seemed doubly attractive, and for several years I engaged in gardening. By way of quick delivery, I possessed an ox team, while my market lay wherever buyers were to be found. I made one trip with my vegetables as far away as the mountains of Trinity.

Later I sold out and went into the cattle business. In 1861, snow fell in the valley to the depth of six inches and lay on for two weeks. That snow put me out of the cattle business.

During these years Indians were numerous. Those who infested the region where I lived were called Mill Creeks or Deer Creeks, the rough canyons of these two streams offering thousands of hiding places to these wild bands. During the winter of 1857 they caused much uneasiness among the settlers. Many raids were made into the valley, followed always by swift retreats into the hills. People were killed, dwellings burned, and stock driven off. These depredations occurred usually along the edge of the valley, but extended on some occasions as far as the Sacramento River.

This state of things could not continue. The Indians, with the accustomed stealth of savages, always made their attacks unexpectedly. Since the settler could not guard against surprise, it was decided to retaliate by carrying the war into the Indians' own territory.

Jack Spaulding, who claimed to have had experience in fighting the reds, organized a party of fifteen men for the purpose of following the marauders into the hills. Hi Good and myself were members of this party. Good, whose acquaintance with the hills was extensive, was elected Lieutenant, while Spaulding acted as Captain.

We knew that to beat the savages we must outplay them at their own game; therefore, we traveled by night, lying over in the daytime. Passing northeasterly over the foothills we kept to the broad ridge between Deer Creek and Mill Creek, this being the ridge along which the Lassen Trail leads.

After two night of travel we reached old Bluff Camp, which was one of the stopping places of the early emigrant trains. It lies in the midst of a vast forest just over the ridge on the Mill Creek slope.

Here we found considerable snow still lying on the cool floor of the pinery, and signs of the Indians were numerous. They had been about the spring in considerable numbers, and the greenest scout in our

party could easily discover their trails leading
through the forest.

We were taken into a steep, sheltered ravine,
where it was thought we would be hidden; then Good
and Spaulding set out on a still hunt to try and locate the Indians' camp.

Our leaders had been gone but a short time when
the mountains on both sides of us suddenly began to
blaze with rifle shots, the reports booming heavily
through the dense forest. The Indians had taken
the first trick. To say that we were a startled lot of
man-hunters would be to put it mildly. I frankly
admit that I was ready to run four ways at once.
Our retreat was a scramble for first place. I had
another man's rifle and someone else had mine. A
companion and I were streaking it up the hill, slip-
ping on the pine needles and making, it seemed to us,
about as much progress backward as forward. The
bullets of the Indians were playing lively tunes
about our ears. Suddenly a small pine limb, clipped
off by a piece of lead, fell just over the other man's
head, and at the same instant he fell flat and lay
limp. I sprang toward him, reached down and
clasped his body in my arms, determined to do my
best to rescue his body; but I felt his sides shaking
convulsively in my hands and in a second he had
rolled over, laughing heartily, and asked:

"What's the rush? What the devil are you running for?"

His fall was due to the pine needles and not to
a bullet.

When we had finally gathered together at the
head of the hollow and had taken a hasty inventory
of our numbers, our excitement was in no wise al-
layed. One man was gone! The Indians had got a
scalp!

There was nothing to do but to return to the
scene of the ambush and make a search for the body.
The Indians had stopped firing now and, of course,
were nowhere to be seen. Slowly and cautiously we
crept back down the ravine, peering and peeping,
and ready to shoot at the first thing that moved, or
to run at the first sound, we hardly knew which.
But, behold! at last we found our missing comrade,
sitting placidly upon a rock and wondering where
the profanely qualified nation we had been! He was
extremely deaf and swore that he had not heard a
single shot nor seen an Indian.

Good and Spaulding soon came running up, as
ready for retreat as the rest of us. As soon as we
got into something like order, the Indians melted
away, but the surprise had taken all the hunt out of
us for the time.

: The next morning we started for the valley, the
Indians hanging on our flanks and rear, clear to the
edge of the hills. Many times, as we topped a ridge
and looked back, we could see our dusky pursuers
peering over the last ridge behind us and keeping
tab upon our movements. It was useless to attempt
to lead them into an ambush, for they knew our
exact number, and as we wound up the slope ahead
of them they would make their count, and if our full

number was not in sight would make a detour around the intervening ravine.

We were gone on this expedition four days, and on our return had to draw pretty freely upon our imaginations for stories that would satisfy our friends.

After this, I became better acquainted with Hi Good. He lived near me on Deer Creek, and we were together on several of the subsequent Indian hunts. We both thought that the savages would be encouraged by our failure to beat them, and warned our neighbors to be on the alert.

Our surmises were correct. In a short time a neighbor's barn was visited in the night and four very valuable mules spirited away. The Indians had a habit of stealing all horses and mules that they could lay their hands on, driving them into the hills and butchering them. Perhaps they preferred them to cattle, because with them they could beat a more hasty retreat; but it always seemed to me as if they liked horse-flesh better than beef and mule-flesh better than either.

Upon receiving word of this last robbery, Good and I enlisted as helpers a young man named Jones and another named George Carter, and started for the hills. These young men seemed to have plenty of nerve, especially Jones, who had been with us on the former hunt and who, I believe, was the coolest man of the party when the surprise came.

We advanced swiftly into the hills, picked up the Indians' trail, and, the second day out, located

their camp. They were snuggled away near the bed
of Dry Creek, well up toward the head of that
stream, but still several miles below the pinery.

We promptly made an attack. We were sheltered
behind bowlders, while the Mill Creeks were partial-
ly protected by a cave. However, we had obtained
a position from which we could shoot directly into
the cave and it was not long until we had them
moving.

We got no Indians, but recaptured considerable
stolen plunder. They had killed the mules. On this
and subsequent hunts we learned that the crafty
fellows made a practice of secreting their supply of
"jerked" mule-meat or other provisions in some
spot at a distance from where they camped, so that
if their camp were surprised their food would still
be safe, and in all the years that I followed them
I never but once found their hidden meat-house.

We returned home much elated with our success.
Indeed, it put quite a bunch of feathers in our caps
when compared with our previous attempt.

CHAPTER II.

THE "Boys in the Hills," as the Indians were frequently called, were not at all satisfied with such an ending of their raid, so soon left another midnight mark upon the whites. Our only chance to reach them was through a surprise, so we permitted several small raids to go by unnoticed, in order that our chances of springing a surprise would be strengthened.

In fact, the depredations continued all through the winter of '57 and '58, and finally complaints were made to General Kibbey, who was then stationed at Sacramento, and a company of troopers was sent up the river by steamboat. They disembarked at Tehama and caused quite a ripple of excitement in that thriving river town by the glitter of their arms and uniforms.

Hi Good and I went to see them after they had made camp, and both of us came to the conclusion that they might be successful in an open country, but that there was little chance of their capturing any Indians in the hills.

Our conclusions proved to be well-founded. The troops, well-mounted, marched gallantly out across the plains and swept up the slope of the hills in fine military array. Their first search seemed to be

directed to finding a good camping place, but before
they found it the Mill Creeks found them, and back
to the valley they marched, making rather better
time than on the upward march.

As a matter of course, this encouraged the "Boys
in the Hills." Again the troops made an advance
and again they were surprised and forced to retreat. This occurred several times, and the soldiers
finally gave it up as a bad job and quit the game.

From this time onward it seemed as though the
Indians never let a chance slip to do the whites damage. Affairs went on in this way until the spring
of 1859, when the raids became so frequent that the
valley was thoroughly roused. It was decided to
raise a subscription among the settlers in order to
get means to carry on an exhaustive campaign
against the renegades, a number of atrocious murders having by this time been added to the list of
the Indians' misdeeds.

A fund of three thousand dollars was secured and
placed, I think, in the hands of a man named Cohen.
Cohen was a merchant who conducted a store at the
Mayhew stage station on Deer Creek. Hi Good, John
Breckenridge and myself, together with William
Simmons, John Martin, John McCord, one Cartin
and a man whom we called "Slim," were selected
and engaged to hunt the red men for two months.
This gave us a company of six to press the chase,
with two to care for our pack animals and attend
camp. We had two mules and a horse to carry our
supplies, but no animals to ride, for we knew that

the trail we were about to follow would lead us into the wildest and most rugged gorges of the Northern Sierras.

Learning of our intended expedition, General Kibbey sent Captain Burns of the army to take command of our party. He arrived in good time and we started on June the 15th. It was, I think, the hottest day I ever experienced in the Sacramento Valley. Many of the old settlers will remember the time, as it was the day that old Tehama burned.

We marched across the dreary, lava-capped foothills on the south side of Deer Creek, and the first day's march proved Captain Burns' unfitness for the task before us. He became completly exhausted, and was sent back to the valley from Deer Creek Flats, where we had made our first camp, and that ended his participation in the two months' hunt.

Left to our own resources, we elected Breckenridge captain and pressed forward. The Indians were evidently well posted as to our movements and intentions, for they secreted their squaws and papooses in the most hidden recesses of the mountains and then proceeded to lead us a merry chase through the dark forests and rugged canyons.

McCord was well acquainted with the hills, and with one companion he usually moved camp, often taking roundabout ways to reach points which the balance of us gained by following the routes taken by the Indians.

Our first separation from our train occurred at the Flats. McCord and companion went by way of the ridge up which the Campbell Trail now leads, crossed Deer Creek at about the point now known as the Polk place, and thence moved northward to Bluff Camp. The rest of us, with provisions enough to last two days, crossed Deer Creek near the mouth of Sulphur Creek, climbed the north wall of the canyon, and so on across Digger Pine Flat and to the pinery about in the region of the Moak Trail.

At Bluff Camp we rejoined McCord. After holding a council, Breckenridge decided that it was best to send a scouting party up the Lassen Trail as far as Deer Creek Meadows, in hopes of picking up the Indians' trail. Our entire party moved up the ridge past Lost Camp and on over what is called the Summit, although it is no real water divide, and down into the cold valley of Onion Creek. This stream is named from the patches of wild onions that are found here and there along its course.

Here we left our camp, while Breckenridge, Hi Good and myself, with the two mules, pushed on to Deer Creek Meadows. We found no Indian signs, but as we approached the level, grassy floor of the meadow we spied five grizzly bears busy among some rotten logs that lay near a cluster of tamaracks. At once we proposed a bear hunt. Breckenridge consented, providing that he could engineer the sport. Hi and I agreed to this, as our acquaintance with grizzlies was very limited.

Accordingly the captain led the pack animals back into the heavy timber which covered the surrounding mountains and grew to the very edge of the meadow. Tying them securely he returned and directed us each to pick out a convenient tree that we were sure we could climb in case of necessity. After providing ourselves, like prudent soldiers, with our means of retreat, we slipped forward a short distance, keeping out of sight of the bears behind a big log. Breckenridge was to take the first shot, and he told us to hammer away at the bear he should shoot until it was done for. The affair had to be handled quite differently to what it would today, as we had none but muzzle-loading rifles and six-shooters.

When all were ready, Breckenridge threw a shot into a huge grizzly and it ripped at its side with its teeth and sent up a terrific bellow. Hi and I let go at the wounded beast and we soon had it down and out. Then on to the next. For a time we were kept mighty busy loading and firing, but the bears never seemed to know where the shots were coming from, and so our trees were not put to use. We killed four and sent the fifth one off badly crippled.

They were huge creatures, weighing, I should judge, a thousand pounds each. We carefully removed their galls, which we knew we could sell to Chinamen. The Chinese use them in preparing some kind of medicine and in those days often paid as high as fifteen dollars apiece for them. The feet we also lopped off. They were to serve as food. After being roasted in hot ashes they make a most tooth-some dish. The sixteen feet made a considerable pack in themselves. The carcasses and skins we left.

CHAPTER III.

FINISHING our bear hunt, we returned to Onion Creek and our entire party then moved back to Bluff Camp. Having failed to strike Indian signs up-country, we decided to swing down into Mill Creek Canyon and cross toward Black Butte on the north side of that stream.

On that day's march, Williams and I had charge of the pack animals. While making our way along the steep side of the canyon we came to a slide full of loose shale. To climb above or below it seemed a hopeless task, so we quickly decided to attempt to hustle our animals across it. We made a brisk start, but in a moment packs and animals, men and guns were tumbling and bouncing and rolling toward Mill Creek at a rate that would have established a record, I am sure, if there had been a stop-watch present to time our speed. Our pack animals got out of the scrape with nothing worse than a few bruises, but I was less fortunate, as I wrenched my ankle badly and for a time was in great pain.

We crossed to the north side of the creek and made camp. Being unfit for scouting duty, I was left with McCord to tend camp, while the balance of the party separated, three going up and three down the canyon to look for sign. They remained away all night.

We were camped on a point some distance up from the creek, the stream forming a bend around the foot of the point. As is usual in this rough canyon, the point ended in a series of cliffs. During the evening we heard chopping, and after a time a tree fell. We were speculating about the matter, and in the meantime keeping outside the circle of light cast by our little fire, when a rifle shot suddenly rang out and a bullet spat into our camp. We seized our rifles and prepared for a brush, but our stealthy foes kept out of sight, though they continued to throw lead in the direction of our camp until well into the night. However, no damage was done except to interfere with a good night's sleep.

Next morning we made an investigation and found that a large party of Indians had been camped under the cliffs only a few hundred yards below us, and that a tree had been thrown across the creek to afford them a bridge to the south side. The camp had evidently been occupied by the women and children, with only a few men, but of course the entire party was now gone.

When Breckenridge returned, we made our report and took him down to the deserted camp. As soon as he found that the runaways were women and children, he said:

"Let them go; we must find the warriors."

Again scouting parties were sent out. Although my ankle was still somewhat stiff and swollen, I was able to make pretty fair headway along the rough and rocky hillsides. I went down the canyon and

after traveling a mile or more discovered a fresh
trail leading northward toward the head of Paynes
Creek. It had been made by warriors, fully a dozen
in number.

I reported to our captain and our plans were
quickly made. The pack animals were sent around
by a devious course to meet us again at Battle Creek
Meadows, while we followed the trail.

We were beginning by this time to get an under-
standing of the signs by means of which the Indians
regulated their movements, and this knowledge later
became of great use to us. For instance, they were
traveling toward the north. On top of the first ridge
that the trail crossed would be found three stones
piled one upon another on some rock. This meant
that the party was to come together for camp or
other purposes in the third canyon beyond. On the
next ridge would be two stones placed in the same
way upon a wayside bowlder, and on the next one.
Thus, a party, finding a monument of stones, had but
to count the stones in order to know where the meeting place was to be, and immediately, if there were
a number together, they would scatter, each man to
himself, only to congregate later at the appointed
place. After we once learned to read these signs,
much tedious trailing was saved us, for we had but
to count the intervening ridges, as the Indians did,
and devote our close work to the final hollow.

We made the advance to Battle Creek Meadows
without mishap. The beautiful little valley was at
this time a perfect sea of tall grass, in the midst of

which, along the winding streams, were magnificent
beds of wild strawberries; yet the forest surrounding the meadows was still streaked with drifts of
snow.

In the edge of the meadow we found where the
Indians had camped. As well as we could read the
signs, they were two nights ahead of us. They had
left a couple of green bear skins lying beside their
extinguished fire.

It was near the end of the day when we discovered the abandoned camp, and, as our pack train had
not yet arrived, we decided to try to get some veni-
son and at the same time endeavor to discover which
way the Indians had taken on departing.

Good and Simmons went up the creek, while Williams and I went down. Simmons shot at and
wounded a bear. It chased him and he yelled for Hi
to shoot it. Before the latter could come up, however, Simmons was so closely pressed that he con-
cluded his time had come. He had not been able to
reload his rifle and there was no tree close by that
he could climb. Finally, when the bear was close
upon him, he stopped and the beast, instead of clos-
ing in on him, immediately began to circle around
him, growling savagely. Hi came up, and afterwards
declared that it was equal to a one-ringed circus to
see Simmons turning cautiously around so as to keep
his face to the circling beast. After enjoying the
show for a while, Hi threw a shot into the bear, and
it made for the timber, badly crippled.

Meanwhile, Williams and I had been having our

share of the fun. We were traveling along close to
the willows that fringed the creek, when a large,
barren doe sprang up. We both shot at her and one
of our bullets broke her hip. I followed the deer
into the willows, without stopping to reload my rifle,
and, soon catching sight of her, finished her with a
shot from my six-shooter. As I was threshing through
the brush to where she lay, Williams suddenly
shouted :

"Look out for that bear!"

I whirled about and beheld a huge grizzly stalk-
ing deliberately through the willows, not fifty feet
away. Without stopping to consider what I was
doing, I cut loose with my revolver, and down the
big beast went, slashing the ground with his teeth.
In a second he was up, and I fired again and down he
went a second time. So a third and a fourth bullet I
threw into him, and then it abruptly dawned upon
me that I had but one bullet lift in my six-shooter
and none in my rifle. Luckily, the bear paid no attention whatever to me. In fact, it appeared not to
have seen me. Williams now gave it a shot from his
rifle and it put off through the willows. The next
morning we found it lying dead not far away.

The pack animals joined us that night, but our
provisions were too low to warrant us in starting
on a long chase, so four of us were sent over toward
Hot Spring Valley to hunt for deer. We got five,
and, returning to camp, were busy "jerking" the
meat, when some of our scouts discovered the Indians' trail leading out toward the Lassen Buttes.

CHAPTER IV.

SIX of us promptly set out upon the trail, carrying each four days' rations, and a hard run we had of it. Up through the heavy forest to the lofty backbone west of what is now called the Morgan Springs Valley, along this high ridge until we had reached the upper timber line, and still onward and upward until we found ourselves upon Lassen's snow-capped peak. The trail led directly past the Buttes, west of the dreary lava of the Cinder Cone region and on toward the unmapped canyon of Pitt River.

On the border of that turbulent stream the redskins doubled on us, and once more we were headed toward the south. Our camp had been ordered to return to Black Buttes on Mill Creek, and to await us there. Coming back on a course much farther west than that followed on the outward trip, we came upon a sawmill out in the region northeast of Red Bluff. There great excitement prevailed. The skulking Indians, preceding us by a day, had run upon one of the bull-punchers near the mill, had killed him and chased his team over a cliff.

Some of the lumber-jacks were trying to find the Indians, while others seemed to be afraid that the Indians would find them. Our provisions were gone, so we went to the cook-house and demanded food. We got what we asked for and hurried onward, the trail still leading us toward the south.

During these severe days our rations consisted principally of sugar. Each man could carry enough to last him several days, and, eked out with manzanita berries, this ration really kept us in good strength. The time ordinarily spent in cooking was saved and gave us that much more time for the business of following the trail. We soon got in the habit of keeping our hunger appeased by frequently dipping into our little sugar sacks, and not infrequently followed the trail for ten or even twelve hours at a stretch without a single stop of more than a few minutes' duration. When it grew too dark for us to read the ground sign, we had but to scrape together a pile of leaves or pine needles and sleep until daylight should come again, and then proceed on our way.

We crossed Mill Creek and Deer Creek and followed the trail as far as the Keefer ridge, between Rock Creek and Chico Creek. Our provisions were by this time completely exhausted, so we returned to the valley for more.

While in the valley a message reached us from the Butte Creek country, warning us to follow the Indians no farther, and stating that a company of fifteen miners would be waiting for us if we persisted in the pursuit. We had always felt certain that the Mill Creeks procured arms and ammunition through friendly relations with whites. This note of warning seemed to settle the matter, and to indicate where the whites in question were to be found.

We thought it best to secure reinforcements before making another advance. My brother, Jack, who lived with me on Deer Creek, and a man named Bates joined our force. We returned to the hills and made camp at a little spring near the present site of the Cole place on the Cohasset ridge.

Believing that the Indians were reinforced, not only by the fifteen miners, but by some of the Butte Creek Indians as well, we now used every precaution in trailing them. Hi Good and I did most of the scouting. One of us would follow the ground sign, while the other acted as lookout to avoid running into an ambush. We had to do most of our work by daylight, but the balance of the party moved only at night.

Crossing Chico Creek Canyon, we reached the ridge beyond, and finally discovered what seemed to be a large camp at or near the present site of the Forest Ranch. After a careful study of the ground, we returned to our camp. On this return trip we ran upon an Indian scout, and after a long, hard chase, killed him. We carried his scalp to camp with us, this being the first trophy we had taken in the campaign.

Upon receiving our report, Captain Breckenridge at once gave orders for an advance. Of course, we had to move in the night. It was a weary climb out of Chico Creek Canyon in the darkness, but we made it and succeeded in surrounding the hostile camp before daylight. Our number being limited and having a pretty large circle to form, it left us separated, man from man, by spaces of about seventy-five yards.

I had been assigned to a position eastward of the camp and very close, as I afterward learned, to the trail which led toward the mining village at the forks of Butte Creek. The forest trees afforded us ample hiding places and we had been ordered to hold our fire until it was perfectly light. Hi Good was on my right and Brother Jack upon my left.

As the gray dawn melted into daylight, the outlines of the camp became clearer. It was evidently a permanent meeting place, as there were signs of its having been frequently occupied. Directly in front of me and standing something like a hundred yards apart were two lofty pine trees, trimmed of branches except for small tufts of foliage on their tops, and, what was my surprise, as the heavens grew brighter, to behold a large American flag depending from the top of each tree.

The Indians, as we afterward learned, had been enjoying a celebration in company with their friends from Butte Creek, and did not prove to be early risers. The sun had crept up to the tops of the pines on the hill east of us before there was any stir in the camp. Then a man emerged from a cluster of little firs and came shuffling up the trail directly toward where I lay. Captain Breckenridge had not yet given the signal to commence firing, so I slipped around my tree in order to remain hidden. As the man approached and passed me, I perceived that he was not an Indian, but a Spaniard. However, birds flocking together on this occasion were to be considered birds of a feather. The man had got but

a few paces past me when Hi Good spied him. In a
moment Good's rifle spoke, and the Spaniard,
wounded, sprang back toward the camp. As he ran
another rifle over on the other side of our circle
cracked, and he fell dead.

The camp was roused. In a twinkling, up the
Indians sprang, men, women and children, and as if
with one impulse they swarmed up the slope directly
toward where I lay. In a moment I was enveloped
in the wild stampede. I shot and then clubbed my
rifle and struggled against the rush. Good and Jack
came to my assistance, and together we turned them
back. The balance of our party were pouring shots
into them and they soon began to seek shelter amid
the logs and thickets of small forest trees.

Our orders from Breckenridge had been to allow
no one to break through the circle, but to spare the
women and children. This was a most difficult pro-
gram to carry out. The bucks were armed and were
returning our fire. The squaws soon perceived that
we were seeking to spare their lives, and so they
clung to the bucks. This made it difficult to get a
bead upon the one without endangering the other.
Seeing that this state of affairs would not do, we sent
word from man to man around to the captain and
asked him for new orders. Soon the word came
back: "Let the squaws and children pass out."

Good, who could speak the Indian dialect,
promptly shouted the order to the Indians. They
eagerly seized upon the suggestion, but we were
soon to learn that the order was a serious mistake.

A warrior would wrap himself in a blanket, throw another blanket or a basket over his head, with a rifle concealed next his body, seize a child by the hand, or hoist one upon his back, and go shuffling past us.

Soon we came in possession of the camp. There was not a bad Indian to be found, but about forty good ones lay scattered about.

While rejoicing over our victory, shots began to ring out and bullets to sing about our ears, and we suddenly found ourselves where so lately we had had the Indians. They were shooting at us from all sides. I heard Hi Good cursing like a wagon-master and saw him trying to get a bead on an Indian. He was behind a tree, from both sides of which pieces of bark were flying as from a woodman's ax. However, our luck had not deserted us. Not one of our party was hit. We charged and scattered the Indians, then kept out guards while we prepared and ate our breakfasts.

Two barrels, partly filled with whiskey, were in the camp, as well as other evidences which pointed to the fact that whites had joined with the redskins in the recent celebration. We soon took our departure for our own camp across Chico Creek, each man well burdened with plunder from the captured camp. I had found three good six-shooters, which I thrust under my belt, thinking these to be about as useful as anything to be had.

CHAPTER V.

WE were filing down the hill into Chico Creek Canyon, and were perhaps a little careless of our advance, when we ran suddenly into an ambush. Six or seven of the Mill Creeks, undoubtedly part of those who had escaped from the camp, had hidden along the trail and, suddenly rising above the birch brush, let us have it. We were strung along in single file. Six of our party were ahead of me, and I suddenly saw them all go down. However, not one was hurt. The Indians disappeared in an instant. In the one glimpse I caught of them I threw up my rifle and fired. I saw one fall with a broken thigh, and sprang after him. Just as I leaped the man behind me fired and the powder from his rifle blackened my right ear. Sliding and crawling down the steep hillside, the wounded Indian could travel nearly as fast as I could. I chased him nearly to the bottom of the canyon before I finished him. The chase cost me my three new six-shooters, all of which were pulled from my belt by the clinging brush.

I rejoined the balance of the party and we had pushed on well down to the creek, when we discovered five of the Indians far above us upon a cliff on the north wall of the canyon. For a few minutes we discussed the probabilities of their being the same party which had ambushed us. Some of our party believed that they were not Indians at all.

During the discussion, I was standing looking upward, the left side of my head touching an oak tree. All at once I saw a puff of smoke arise from the distant cliff, and in a moment I was down and out. A bullet had cut in between my head and the oak, driven my scalp full of bark, and left me senseless for twenty minutes. The scar from that shot forms a very considerable bald spot on my head today.

We returned to our camp on the Keefer ridge. A man by the name of King at that time had a sawmill a few miles farther up the ridge. Just after we reached camp, two teamsters drove up the old road toward this mill. One of them was my old friend, Perry McIntosh, the other a man named Lindsay. I told Breckenridge that some of us ought to overtake the teamsters and guard them to the mill, as the Indians were likely to overhaul them. The captain thought that the trip to the mill could be made in safety.

However, it was not. The Indians, sure enough, spied the teamsters, waylaid them, and shot Lindsay. McIntosh escaped, reached the mill, and later rescued Lindsay, who subsequently recovered.

News of the fight at Forest Ranch quickly reached the valley, and for a time exaggerated stories were in circulation to the effect that our entire party had been killed. Coon Garner raised a party of fifteen and hastened into the hills to look us up. If I remember correctly, P. M. Guynn and Dan Sutherland are the only surviving members of that party.

We had moved back across Chico Creek, and Garner's party found us encamped near the site of the Doe Mill. We had revisited the battle-ground at Forest Ranch, only to find that the surviving Indians had returned and burned the bodies of their slain.

We were not yet satisfied with the state of affairs at the forks of Butte Creek. Scouting through that canyon we jumped some Indians, who promptly ran for the bottom of the canyon. Our enlarged party at once swarmed down the hillside toward the mining town. Breckenridge had ordered us to kill any Indian found even in the streets of the village, but to shoot none who had sought shelter within the houses.

Some of the fleeing Indians headed straight for the village. Knowing a short course to a footbridge where I believed they would cross the stream, I called to Williams and together we raced to that point. We succeeded in tumbling several Indians off the bridge into the creek as they sought to cross.

Then we entered the village. The Indians were there in considerable numbers, but all had prudently disappeared within the houses. A man named Wallace conducted a store. He resented our appearance, and, stepping outside his store, shouted to us that if a single Indian were killed he would follow us up and kill six white men. As soon as Breckenridge entered the town, I reported Wallace's remark.

"Point out that man to me!" said he, abruptly.

"He is standing back of that counter, and has two six-shooters beside him," replied I.

"Can you cover him from where you stand?"

I answered that I could, and at once threw my gun on the man. Breckenridge entered the store, strode up to Wallace, and told him very plainly why we had followed the Indians to Butte Creek. He declared that we had long suspected and now had proof that the Mill Creeks received support from either the Butte Creek Indians or the miners, or both, and that the arms and ammunition secured in this way were used to murder white people of the country farther north. Breckenridge was not a pleasant man to have for an enemy, and Wallace had departed very far from his boastful, threatening manner before the former was through with him.

We learned later that the store-keeper's squaw had received a wound in the Forest Ranch fight, which fact probably accounted for the stand Wallace took. In the course of the controversy, he remarked that if we had been a day earlier at Forest Ranch we would have found him at the camp, to which he received the comforting reply that if such had been the case he would surely have met with exactly the same treatment as that accorded the Indians.

All this time a group of Indians was stationed in back part of the store. After Breckenridge had freed his mind to Wallace, I told some of the boys to keep an eye on the store-keeper, as I wished to take a look at an Indian whom I had seen in the back

room. This Indian was seated upon a keg. I had
recognized him as a young fellow whom I had shot
down during the Forest Ranch fight, thinking him
dead, only to find him missing after the battle.

I approached him now and asked him how he
felt, to which he made no reply. I was curious to
learn just how much an Indian could endure in the
way of a gun-shot wound. I pulled his shirt up over
his head and there were the wounds, indicating that
my bullet had entered his right breast and passed
out under his left shoulder-blade. The bullet must
have been deflected in some way, since a straight
line drawn from one wound to the other would have
pierced his heart; yet here he sat, apparently in good
health, three days after the battle!

We moved camp to a ridge some miles below the
forks and spent several days trying to straighten out
affairs with the Indians of Butte Creek. We captured a chief called "The Old Captain," and, as soon
as he found himself within our power, he professed
to be very friendly and assured us that if we would
but lie low for a time he and his men would capture
the remainder of the Mill Creeks for us.

I had no faith whatever in the old fellow, or in
his protestations of friendship; but Breckenridge
seemed to think that he could be trusted, or at least
that it was our duty to give him a trial. As a sort
of hostage, we kept "The Old Captain" in our camp
while a young Indian of his clan, called "Tony,"
was sent out to muster the warriors. He returned
with about fifteen of them, and they spent several

days in our midst. They declared that the proper way to get the Mill Creeks was to slip up on them and fight in the old style of Indian warfare,—that is, with bows and arrows. During several days they made much ado of practicing with these ancient weapons, and I must do them the credit of saying that some of them shot extremely well. Finally a war party set out, under the leadership of "Tony," "The Old Captain" still being held as hostage.

The chief's squaw was allowed to visit him, and she came and went at will, thus, of course, keeping him in communication with the rest of his people, those who pretended to be on the warpath included. During the day he was allowed to roam about our camp, but at night he was lodged in a vacant cabin that stood near, one man being detailed to guard him.

One night, after Tony's party had been several days gone, the old rascal pretended to be very sick, and finally prevailed upon his guard to lead him some distance from the cabin. They had barely got beyond the bounds of the sleeping encampment when the Indian made a sudden break for liberty. The guard gave chase, and after a hundred-yard dash overhauled him and brought him back. Thereafter he was secured by ropes.

This action of the chief convinced Breckenridge of my way of thinking regarding the trickery of the Butte Creeks, so it was decided to hunt up the pretended war party and see what they were up to. The following morning we split up into scouting par-

ties and set out. Ad Williams and I made a search
of the canyon in the direction of Hell Town. We
were advancing along the ridge, from which we
could keep a sharp lookout into the ravines below
and upon the opposite wall of the canyon. I finally
spied some figures far below us, and on the opposite
side of the creek. They soon disappeared within a
dense thicket, and, not long afterward, we were able
to make out a faint ribbon of smoke curling up above
the brush.

We decided to investigate, so slid cautiously
down the hillside, crossed the creek, and, creeping
into the thicket, found seven of our Butte Creek
"allies" lounging idly about a tiny fire. Tony was
among the number. We lost no time in making
them our prisoners and starting with them back to
camp.

While we were toiling up the hill, within perhaps
a mile of our destination, we suddenly heard a fusil-
lade of shots coming from the direction of our camp.
The shooting continued for some time, those engaged
seeming to be moving toward the breaks of the canyon, the last shot or two being fired over the slope
of the ridge.

We soon reached camp and learned the cause of
the disturbance. Those of our party who were in
camp had been scattered carelessly about, paying
no heed to "The Old Captain," who suddenly
jumped free from his ropes, gave a triumphant
whoop, and started like a deer toward the canyon.
He had secured a knife in some way, cut his bonds

beneath his blanket, and then made his second break for liberty.

None of the Whites had their rifles at hand, but most of them promptly drew their six-shooters and opened on the scudding red man. His rush was so sudden, however, that he escaped the first scattering volley and outstripped all his pursuers excepting Hi Good, who was swift of foot and had great powers of endurance.

Good continued to run and shoot without bringing the Indian down, until he had emptied his revolver. Not being able to reload on the run, he swept onward with his weapon empty, and, getting close enough soon after crossing the brow of the hill, he threw his revolver and knocked the Indian down. Before the latter could recover, Good overhauled him and soon after returned with him to camp. The chief had been shot twice in the chase and was so badly wounded that when we moved away we left him to the care of his squaw. I think that he subsequently recovered.

CHAPTER VI.

ANOTHER incident that occurred while we were encamped at this place might be worthy of mention. Two of our party, Bates and a man named Wash Cox, the latter being of Garner's party, returned one day from a hunting trip and said that they had killed two bears and left them hanging in a tree. They wished someone else to go after the carcasses. I agreed to bring in the meat, and set out at once.

On reaching the spot to which they had directed me, however, I was surprised and disgusted to find two fat hogs awaiting me. After debating the situation in my own mind for a time, I finally decided to carry the meat to camp, as I had promised. Immediately on reaching camp, however, I reported the affair to Breckenridge, and told him that it looked like a slippery trick, to get someone else besides the real culprits involved.

The captain looked at the matter in the same light as myself, and he lost no time in calling Bates and Cox before him. He told them that he would not countenance any such thievery and ordered them to hunt up a man named Harris, to whom it was found the hogs belonged, pay him for the animals, and that then they would be drummed out of camp as unfit members of our party.

The two men left camp and stayed away for
some time. When they returned they asserted that
they had found Harris and offered him pay for the
hogs, which he refused. This may have been true,
but it did not lessen the offense of having killed the
animals.

The second part of the men's sentence had yet to
be carried out, Garner having agreed with Breckenridge in the matter. Hi Good, as our second in command, was left to carry the order out. He com-
manded Bates and Cox to move, and ordered the rest
of us to provide all the music that could be coaxed
out of the pots and pans of our camping outfit. The
rest of us were ready for our parts, but now a halt
came in the proceedings, for Bates entered a strong
protest. He swore that he would not be driven out
of camp in this way and that there were not enough
of us to force him to go. He stepped up to Good and
struck him and in a moment the two were fighting
desperately. Bates was a powerful man and for a
time it looked as though he would master his man,
but Good's endurance was the greater and he at
length knocked Bates down and was beating him
cruelly when I stopped him. Then the two men were
drummed out of camp, according to orders.

The recaptured Butte Creeks tried to explain
their failure to do as promised by pretending that
they had overtaken the Mill Creeks and been
whipped. They now promised to go with us and
lead us to the hiding places of the renegades. I considered this promise as little likely to be fulfilled as

the former one, but it was decided to give the Indians another trial.

Accordingly, it was arranged that the balance of the party were to march through the hills to the Sidoros place on Rock Creek, while Hi Good and I should bring the seven captive Indians directly to the valley, thence move northward along the edge of the valley to the same point. We traveled as rapidly as we could, but night overtook us when we were but a short distance north of Chico Creek. We decided to lie over till morning. We halted beneath a large oak and I said to Hi:

"You guard the Indians the first half of the night and I'll take the last half; or turn it about, just as you like."

"Guard be d——d!" said Good. "I'm going to sleep."

And he proceeded to snuggle down on the ground. I told him that the Indians would knock us on the head and skip out to join the Mill Creeks as sure as we both slept, but he declared that they wouldn't lay a finger upon us. Say what I could he would take no hand in the guarding, so I sat awake all night while he slept. The Indians made no break, either to escape or to harm us, but I have always felt satisfied that the white scalps that they most longed to handle would have been dangling at their belts in short order had I relaxed my vigilance.

Next day we reached the Sidoros place, where the entire party was reunited. After dinner, someone remarked that there was a fine swimming hole up the creek a mile or so. Old man McCord wanted to take a swim. Immediately, Tony, the Indian, asked Breckenridge if he and his party could not go along and shoot some fish with their arrows. Breckenridge consented, and I volunteered to go along, saying that a bath would not hurt me in the least. I was satisfied that the Indians would try to escape.

We reached the swimming hole in due time, and McCord took his bath, while I sat on the bank, the Indians meantime being very intent on their fishing. They got several pike and suckers and appeared to be very much interested in the sport.

After McCord left the water, I stripped and plunged in. I had no sooner struck the water than a whoop rang out, and, like a flash, every Indian leaped into the brush and started to run up the creek. McCord was too slow to stop them. I sprang up the bank, seized my six-shooter and put after them. I chased them for a mile and got only one flying shot, but did no damage. In the course of the chase I suddenly found myself running full tilt past a house that stood amid some trees not far from the creek. There were some members of the household standing in the doorway, doubtless attracted by the scudding Indians. I tortured my naked feet frightfully in the course of that run; nevertheless, I managed to make a wide detour around that house on my return to camp. The last I saw of the Butte Creeks they were streaking it like quails up the hill toward where a section of the Richardson rock-wall now stands.

It was about this time that word came to me that the Indians had visited my place on Deer Creek, burned my house and barn, killed five head of cattle and practically cleaned me out. My brother, Jack, was then living with me. Shortly before this, during a trip to Marysville, he had purchased a seventy-five-dollar suit of clothes. Some time later, up Deer Creek Canyon, I killed an Indian who had on the vest and trousers of that suit.

CHAPTER VII.

IT was decided to give the Mill Creeks another blow. We felt satisfied that those who had escaped from Forest Ranch had joined with another party in Deer Creek. The main party, including Garner's force, was to march back across the foothills and into the pinery as far as Cold Springs, which lies on top of the mountain south of Deer Creek, while scouting parties were looking for fresh Indian sign in the surrounding country.

Ad Williams and I pushed north to Deer Creek and then advanced up the rugged canyon of that stream. On the second day out we struck a fresh trail and that evening located the Indians' camp in the bottom of the canyon, perhaps two miles above where Tom Polk's cabin now stands.

We swung back to Cold Springs and made our report. The main party at once dropped over the ridge into the big canyon and began its slow, cautious march toward the camp. When night fell again we were not more than a mile below the camp. The Indians gave no indications of being alarmed. Our plans were accordingly made for the attack. During the hours of darkness we would creep forward through the steep, tangled ravines, surround the

sleeping Indians, and strike as soon as it became
light enough to draw bead.

The Indians were strung out for some distance
along the south side of the stream. It was broad
daylight before we were opposite the lower ones.
I was advancing with a number of others as rapidly
as possible along the steep hillside, in order to get
on the up-stream side, and was probably midway
of the scattered camp, when a rifle suddenly rang
out from somewhere in the rear of our line. Simmons had spied a dusky form rising above a bowlder
and, thinking that we were discovered, had fired.

The alarmed Indians at once fled up-stream. We
killed a number, but many escaped up that brushy,
bowlder-strewn canyon. In the course of the running fight, I noticed several Indians springing down
a steep bank into the creek. I watched for them to
climb up the farther bank, but none appeared. Other
searchers up and down the stream failed to discover
them, so I decided that the best way to find what had
become of them would be to follow them. I accordingly leaped down the bank into the stream. The
moment I struck the water a gun snapped close behind me, and, glancing back, I beheld a group of the
Indians huddled together in water nearly waist deep
within a cavern that led back under the bank. A
young man called "Billy" was in their midst, and it
was he who had snapped his gun at me. The water
had probably dampened his powder.

I at once called to the men on the bank above that
I had found the runaways, and, throwing my gun on

this Billy, ordered him to march out and surrender. He did so, and all the others, about a dozen in number, followed. They were mostly squaws and children.

Several of our party knew this Billy to be a dangerous and troublesome customer. I kept hold of his wrist after I got up the bank, not intending that he should try any of his slippery tricks upon me. I asked him if he knew who had shot Lindsay, and he gruffly replied:

"I shoot him."

After the ball was over I led Billy up to Breckenridge and said that he had confessed to shooting Lindsay. The captain was a peculiar man. He was usually very deliberate in his movements, but was possessed of great strength. He put the question to the Indian himself, as calmly as a teacher might ask a pupil his name:

"Do you know who shot Lindsay?"

"I shoot him."

And the captain replied, very calmly, "Then I will shoot you," and he proceeded to pull his revolver from its scabbard as leisurely as though he were about to indulge in target practice. As he was raising the weapon, and while its muzzle was still pointing downward, it was discharged. Immediately I let go my hold of the Indian's wrist and slapped my hand to my side. The bullet had struck a stone, glanced upward, bored through the two thicknesses of my heavy belt, and, flattened like a coin, lay burning under my skin. The way I flung off that belt

and tore at that hot lead was certainly not slow, and
afforded some of the boys much merriment.

Meanwhile, the Indian, freed from my grip, had
grappled with Breckenridge and the two were in the
midst of a desperate struggle. Thinking the captain
hard pressed, some of the boys were for rushing to
his assistance, but I waved them back and told them
that any man who was so many kinds of a fool as to
let off his gun accidentally deserved no better treatment than to be killed by a thieving Mill Creek.
However, Breckenridge soon overpowered his foe
and killed him.

After this young Indian was finished, we collected
our prisoners and started down the canyon, but soon
found that there was another member of the tribe
who was bent on making us trouble. This was an
Indian who was called "The Doctor." He was
really a chief. His squaw was in our possession and
the chief certainly put up a game fight against odds.

We had gone but a short distance when he raised
up from behind a rock a short distance ahead and
fired, but his bullet went wild. We gave chase, but
he disappeared, only to repeat his ambush act several
times, always, for some reason, failing to get his
man.

Finally we came to a halt in a plum thicket not
far above the present site of the Polk barn. Most of
the boys were helping themselves to plums, the rest
of us guarding the prisoners. Suddenly the old chief
arose in the very center of that plum thicket and
tried another flying shot. He sank down again im-

mediately, and, in the confusion of the moment, escaped from the thicket, slipped down to the creek,
and crossed. Then from the opposite side of the
stream he continued to shoot at us. We had a pretty
good chance at him now and soon sent him to shelter
in a pile of rocks. It would be a difficult matter for
him to get to another shelter from where he was, so
we kept him in play while Hi Good slipped across
the creek and made a detour to get above him. Soon
Good's rifle cracked and in a moment the Indian's
body came rolling down the steep hillside. His
squaw gave one glance at the lifeless form, then
withdrew her gaze with no sign whatever of excitement or grief. Some of the other squaws, however,
sent up a dismal wail, which was probably the death-
song of their tribe.

Many stories have been circulated regarding a
bear-skin full of watches and coin which this old
"Doctor" is believed to have left within the cave
under the creek bank where the Indians had taken
shelter. There may have been some small founda-
tion in fact for these reports, but I have never believed that there was wealth enough hidden in that
cave to pay a man for the hardships of a trip into
the canyon to get it.

CHAPTER VIII.

RETURNING to the valley, we again made camp on Rock Creek. It was decided that the prisoners should be taken to the Yumalacca Reservation, which lay on the western side of the Sacramento Valley, in the southern part of what is now Tehama county. Hi Good and I made the journey, having hired a team and wagon for the purpose.

Upon our return, our party broke up, the two months for which we had enlisted having expired some time before. Those of us who lived in the Deer Creek country started afoot across the plans toward our homes. We had gone but a couple of miles when we spied an infantry company marching toward the hills. The two parties came together at a point on the plains about one and one-half miles east of my present residence.

We found the soldiers to be under the command of Kibbey. He had learned of our campaign against the Indians, and had come up in person to wind up the affair. He listened attentively to a verbal report of our experiences, and then took down the names of the six of us who had been so long upon the Indian's trail. He said that we would be enrolled in the regular service and should share in all government awards for the duty done. However, that is

the last I have ever heard of the matter. Four of
our party were prevailed upon to go with the soldiers as guides, but Breckenridge and Hi Good and
I went on home.

The history of Kibbey's campaign can be quickly
summed up. He roamed through the mountains for
several weeks, going as far east as the Big Meadows,
where he seized a number of perfectly harmless Indians as prisoners. He returned by way of Butte
Creek, where he got more prisoners, and, proceeding
to Chico, "captured" the Bidwell Indians and trans-
ported the entire lot to the Reservation. He did not
get a single Mill Creek, or any other Indian who had
ever caused the whites any trouble.

General Bidwell promptly went to Sacramento
and gave bonds for the good behavior of his Indians,
whereupon the Government authorities released
them, and they returned to Chico.

The other Indians jumped the Reservation, singly
or in small squads, and drifted back to their former
haunts. Some perhaps became contented with the
life there and remained. However, taken as a move-
ment to rid the foothills of the bad Indians, Kibbey's
campaign was an absolute failure. In one way, it
resulted in making matters worse in our part of the
country, for the more dangerous of the Indians, on
returning from the Reservation, were apt to bring
others of like character with them, and, in this way,
undoubtedly, a number of tough redskins were added
to the bands in the hills.

During the winter of '59 and '60 the raids of the

Indians followed one another with startling swift-
ness and regularity. Scarcely a week passed that
some rancher or stockman did not suffer the loss of
cattle, horses or mules, and every precaution taken
to guard against the slippery red-men proved futile.
Finally, they grew so bold as to pay a visit to Hi
Good's rock corral on Deer Creek and to drive off
some work cattle that belonged to Good and me.

At this time, a young man named Bowman, but
whom we always called "Bully," was living with
Hi. "Bully" had had no experience in fighting Indians, but he seemed a bold young fellow and we had
confidence in him.

The three of us at once set out after the cattle
thieves. We had no difficulty in following their
trail, the Indians having become arrogant through
their recent successes. We trailed them up Dry
Creek and located their temporary camp near the
head of that stream, some distance below the pine
timber.

When discovered, the Indians were engaged in
butchering a part of the stolen cattle. We were on
the opposite side of the ravine from them, and, having a good view of their position, opened fire upon
them. They seized their rifles and returned our fire.
We noticed immediately that they had our range
perfectly, and were dropping their bullets very close
to us. In fact, it was but a few moments until I
heard Good cursing savagely.

"What's the matter?" I called.

"They've plugged me!" he replied, then, between a groan and an oath, added: "I believe my leg's busted."

I made my way to his side and found that he had been shot through the thigh. The wound was very painful and left him for a time almost helpless.

A shout of triumph from the Indians told us that they were aware of their success. The bullets were falling thicker and closer each moment, and I felt certain that we would soon all be picked off unless we could make a speedy change in the course of the battle.

I told Hi to drop down behind a big bowlder, while "Bully" and I should try to force the Indians out of their present position. Good did as I requested, and "Bully" and I made a sudden charge forward. We dashed down the slope, thus placing ourselves on the hillside closer to and below the Indians, and then began our advance toward them by leaping from one shelter to another. Immediately, as I expected, their bullets began to fly high. For a time it was give and take at a lively rate, and I noticed that "Bully" was behaving like a veteran. Since our every rush was toward the front, however, the Indians soon began to give way, and then we hustled them the harder.

As they passed up the hill in retreat, we began to hear Hi's rifle cracking from across the ravine. Soon he set up a shout. We thought that he might be hard pressed, so hurried to him, but found that he only wanted us to assist him to his feet. He was not suffering so badly now, but was unable to walk. We did not carry him, but placed him between us and then had him thrown his arms over our shoulders.

In this manner we made our way over the twenty rough miles of the foothills to the valley. Not only did we support our wounded comrade, but we drove before us four of the oxen that we recovered.

Good's hurt was only a flesh wound, and we were in no particular hurry to reach our homes, as we did not think it necessary to procure the services of a doctor. In a few weeks Good was fully recovered.

Many of the Mill Creeks at this time were good shots. I have frequently found where they have indulged in target practice, and, considering the distances and size of the targets, am convinced that they could shoot as accurately as the average white man. But they possessed two weaknesses that are common to many whites,—once get them rattled, and the danger of their hitting you became lessened by many degrees; and they could not shoot accurately down hill. It was for the first of these reasons, largely, that we always planned to give them a surprise. They invariably outnumbered us and it became necessary to even up matters as much as possible by rattling them in the start.

During these times Ili and I, sometimes with "Bully" and sometimes by ourselves, made many scouting trips into the hills and managed to reduce the number of bad Indians on almost every trip. Still, their numbers remained undiminished as far as we could judge by the damage done, and we became

convinced that they were being constantly re-in-
forced.

I often told Hi that it was a mistake to leave the
squaws in the hills, since it was but natural for the
bucks to find them, and as fast as the latter were put
out of the way, others from the Reservation, or from
more distant parts of the mountains, would take
their places.

CHAPTER IX.

ABOUT the middle of the winter (1859), Hi Good, Carter and I indulged in a sort of wild-goose chase which netted us next to nothing in the way of success, but which brought me nearer death than many close-range gun-fights have since done. Hi had become convinced that we could unearth a winter camp of the Indians by a careful search up Deer Creek Canyon.

At first I opposed his plans, but at last consented to accompany him and Carter. We set out afoot, each carrying his rifle, six-shooter and rations, besides a generous roll of blankets, for the mid-winter season, even in California, does not permit of a bed of dried leaves. I was not yet twenty years of age, and so, of course, was buoyed up by the elasticity of youth. My companions were only a few years older. If I am not mistaken, I was the youngest member of our party in all our principal campaigns against the Indians.

We moved up Deer Creek under threatening skies. For two days we pushed deeper into the canyon, reaching a point rather higher than the Jackson Mine, but found no fresh signs of Indians. The third day out we swung over by Bluff Camp and then, as the inevitable Christmas storm shrouded the gloomy forests and dreary foothills, we tuerned our faces toward the valley.

A bad day we had of it, especially after leaving the shelter of the pines. Rain soaked our clothing, and then came a fine drizzle, half snow, half rain, to chill us to the marrow. A few miles below the timber belt, with the night rapidly drawing on, we halted beside a gnarled digger pine and built a fire. And beside that fire we spent the night,—not sleeping, mind you, nor even lying down, but revolving slowly so that the soaking and roasting processes, going on at the same time on different surfaces of our bodies, might be equally distributed.

Our search so far having proved fruitless, we had ample time during the night to discuss plans for the future. Good argued that the Indians must have moved over into Mill Creek, but along about this time my memory began to inform me very persistently that I had promised to accompany two young ladies on the following night to a dance at Oak Grove, that being the name then applied to the Phillips place on Pine Creek.

Hi finally announced that at break of day we would start for Mill Creek. I told him that he could count me out, as I was going to the dance. He laughed at me, and told me that I would never get there. That made me the more determined that I would, so at daybreak we split, Good and Carter making toward the big canyon to the north, while I started straight for the valley.

It was still raining in torrents. I passed down

the ridge that divides the two principal branches of
Dry Creek, keeping a little over the backbone so as
to be sheltered from the wind. I was striding along,
thinking very little of Indians and very much of
more agreeable objects, when suddenly I shot out
into open view of a large party of the redskins,
snuggled under a drooping cave not sixty yards
away.

They saw me as soon as I them. There was a
general scramble among them for their weapons,
but while they scrambled I slid around the point and
beat a swift retreat up the next ravine. I saw that
I had no business at close range tackling that Christmas party. I did not fire a short, nor did the Indians. Later, when I had gained a loftier position
on the next ridge to the south, I paused long enough
to spy them out once more in the cave, but there
was no evidence to show that they were attempting
a pursuit.

I kept on my course down the slope of the hills
and reached the footlog opposite Good's cabin about
the middle of the afternoon. This log was one that
had been felled as a bridge and then flattened along
the upper surface so as to afford safer footing. I
had crossed it many times and felt no hesitation in
stepping upon it now, although the creek was flowing, a turbulent flood, beneath it.

I had reached the middle of the passage and was
directly over the wickedest part of the current, when
that treacherous log snapped beneath me and in a
second I was being tumbled down a crazy reach of

the stream like a chip,—and not floating, either, for I was under as much as I was above the surface and felt, at times, as though my head were scraping the bottom. I tried to swim, but I might as well have tried to walk on the surface. In fact, in a very short time it dawned upon me that I was drowning. I made a frantic effort to seize something for support, and then, without a touch of real pain, I lost consciousness.

An old man named Dean was at this time living with Good. He had been seated at the cabin gazing out toward the rapidly rising water in the creek. In the course of their journeys up or down the banks his eyes had detected the footbridge, staunch and safe. When next his sight fell upon the same spot, the bridge was gone. This interested him. After musing upon the matter for a time, it slowly dawned upon him that someone might have gone down with the log. He promptly ran to the bank, followed it down-stream for two hundred and fifty yards, and there, in an eddy, spied my body lying next the bank.

He rushed to where I lay, nearly submerged and apparently dead, seized me by the feet and dragged me up the bank. My blankets and six-shooter were still strapped to me, while I grasped my rifle in one hand and a clump of willow bushes in the other. It was perhaps a lucky chance that he drew me out of the water and up the bank feet first, for that caused the water to run from my stomach and lungs and doubtless saved my life.

I soon revived, but felt far from gay. By means of strong draughts of whiskey and of vigorous rubbing I was soon put upon my feet, when I walked home. I accompanied my girl friends to the dance that night, but I did not dance.

It was at this gathering that I first met Mr. Ira Wetherby, who has since become so well and so favorably known to me.

Good and Carter did not get home until the following day, having failed to locate any Indians in the canyon of Mill Creek.

CHAPTER X.

IN June of 1862, the whites of the upper valley were roused as they had never been before by the atrocities of the Mill Creeks. A skulking band swept through the foothills, killing stock, burning cabins, and injuring the whites in every way possible, until they reached the Keefer ridge. There they lay in wait for a teamster, who was hauling for Keefer, and shot him to death beside his team.

Thirsting for more blood, they dropped down into Rock Creek Canyon and slipped toward the valley where a number of settlers lived. Unfortunately, three of the Hickok children were gathering blackberries along the creek side, some distance above their home, which was on the place now known as the Burch ranch. The oldest of the three was a graceful girl of sixteen, the second a girl of fourteen, and the third a boy some years younger.

The two girls were shot to death with arrows, and their bodies left in the bushes beside the stream, while the little boy was dragged away into the hills.

The Indians knew that these murders could not go long unnoticed, as there was considerable travel up and down the Keefer road. In fact, the bodies of the murdered girls were found late in the afternoon of the day on which they were killed, and then indeed were the whites aroused to the danger that so constantly hovered over their homes.

Many parties were raised and hurried into the hills. In fact, the feeling against the Indians was so bitter that it was proposed to make a general clean-up, even of the friendly Indians, of which there were camps at Bidwell's, at Keefer's, and at the Phillips place on Pine Creek; but Mr. Hickok, the bereaved father, forbade this being done on his behalf, and, of course, at such a time, his wishes were respected.

I was asked to take up the chase, but there was sickness in my family at the time and I could not leave home. However, Hi Good and "Bully" responded to the call, and Sandy Young, boss vaquero on the Bidwell Rancho, was of Hi's party. This, I think, was the first occasion on which these two men worked together on an Indian trail.

They traced the Indians northward, past Deer Creek, Dry Creek, and Mill Creek, and finally overhauled them, I think, in the head of Antelope Creek east of Red Bluff. They found the mangled remains of the captured white boy amid signs which indicated that he had been made to move around in a circle, probably being tied, while he was stoned to death by the children of the savages.

The whites made a pretty good clean-up on this occasion. A day or two later I was sitting on my porch when Hi and Sandy rode past on their way home. Hi showed me eight fresh scalps that he had tied to his saddle.

And still the Mill Creeks remained in sufficient

numbers to leave their terrible mark upon the white man's home. Somewhat later, as I recall it, than the killing of the Hickok children, the Indians floated through the hills still farther south, and this time the blow fell upon the Lewis family, who lived in the Clear Creek country, about midway between Chico and Oroville.

As on the former occasion, the blood-thirsty wretches slipped down to the very edge of the valley, and made their attack by stealth upon those who were helpless to defend themselves. The story as it came to me was like this: The three Lewis children, a girl and two boys, were on their road home from school. They had reached a brook and the oldest boy was stooping over to drink, when the hidden Indians shot him through the head, killing him instantly. The girl and younger boy, the latter a little fellow just starting to school, were seized and hustled into the hills. The little boy soon became leg-weary and his brains were dashed out against a rock. The girl was hurried forward until night came on.

The party was then well up on a hillside above a stream. For some reason, a portion of the Indians pushed forward and left the captive in charge of one of their number as guard. This guard seemed especially anxious to be permitted to follow his fellows. He placed the girl upon a large rock, motioned for her to remain there, and then set out a short distance in the direction taken by the other Indians.

The moment his back was turned, the plucky

little girl slid down from the rock, but her keeper
was stealthily watching her. He ran back to her,
seized her and shook her, and, drawing his knife,
made motions as though about to cut her throat.
She cowered and slunk away as if in abject fear, and,
thinking that he had her completely intimidated, he
placed her once more upon the rock and moved
away.

However, the girl's wit had not deserted her.
The Indian had no sooner moved away than she
slipped down from the rock and darted into a little
ravine that creased the hillside. The darkness
favored her. She made her way to the bottom of the
canyon, discovered which way the water was flowing,
and, in spite of the anxious search of the whole party
of Indians, escaped and made her way to the valley.

I think that it was on this same raid that the Indians robbed the home of one "Portugee Al," who
lived in the head of Little Chico Creek, taking,
among other articles, his wife's hat. They also, on
their return toward Mill Creek, robbed a man named
Bolivar, who lived near the present site of the
Richardson Springs.

A party was promptly mustered, of which I was
a member. Sim and Jake Moak of Chico were also
of the party. We struck through the hills and picked
up the Indians' trail south of Deer Creek. It led
down into the deep canyon, crossed Deer Creek just
above the mouth of Sulphur Creek, and headed directly up toward the towering cliff that walls the
gorge on the north.

Just east of the principal cliff is a steep, wedge-like defile, up which it is possible for one to climb to the top. Up this narrow pass we crept single file. Why the Indians did not turn on us and annihilate our entire party has always been a mystery to me, for we found them on the flat just beyond the crest.

They spied us before we were fairly upon them, and away they went, dodging and ducking through the thickets like frightened deer. I brought down one with a short from my double-barrel, but he was up and streaking it through the brush before I could lay hands upon him. Several of us followed him for a half-mile or more down the slope toward Little Dry Creek before we finished him.

We had but one horse with us on this trip, and this animal we left at Sulphur Creek. In the course of the attack and chase, I lost my hat, but among the plunder recaptured from the Indians was found the gaily-beribboned headgear which had been stolen from "Portugee Al's" wife. On the homeward trip, the boys insisted that I should wear the recovered hat, in place of the one I had lost, and that I should ride the horse. I did so, but it can be imagined the figure I presented, wearing that absurd hat and with an Indian scalp tied to my saddle.

CHAPTER XI.

IN August of this year the Indians paid me a friendly call. It was a Sunday morning. Upon arising and stepping out of doors, my attention was at once drawn to a column of smoke curling up from my barn. My neighbors, the Carters, were gone at this time, and the three boys of the family, fearful of a night attack at the hands of the Mill Creeks, had come to my place to sleep.

I immediately shouted to them that the barn was afire and started on a run for the building. One glance inside convinced me that the fire had but recently been started and could be easily stopped. Some loose hay had been flung down in the shed where my horses had been stabled, and fired, but the blaze had not yet reached the mow or taken hold of the building. The glance that told me this informed me likewise that my two horses, that had been left stabled the evening before, were gone.

The bank of the creek was but a couple of rods away. I seized a bucket and sprang toward it. As I dipped up a bucket of water, I perceived Indian tracks leading into the stream. Rocks near the bank were still wet from the wash caused by the hurrying men or beasts. In fact, glancing farther, I saw one of the horses returning toward the stream on the north side.

I returned with the bucket of water and soon had the fire extinguished. By this time the boys were out, so while I secured my rifle and six-shooter, I had one of them run and get up a saddle horse that was loose in the pasture. But on going to the barn to saddle up, I found myself balked, as the two saddles that I had left hanging in the barn were both gone.

I knew that it would be useless to try to ride the animal bareback, as I had tried it several times before, always to meet with defeat; and yet I was not in a humor to neglect the polite attention paid me by the Indians. There was nothing to be done but to take it afoot, and so I started.

Instead of crossing the creek and attempting to overhaul the renegades by means of a stern chase, I ran at top speed up the stream, along the south bank. I reached Hi Good's cabin, after a run of a mile and a half, and hailed him, telling him in as few words as possible what had occurred.

Good snatched up his weapons and joined me. I had run many a half-mile race with Hi, and must admit that I usually took second money, but on this day I was to see him reach the limit of his powers of endurance.

We crossed the creek at the mouth of the canyon, and, still running, pressed up the long slope directly toward the north. We knew that the Indians should be down nearer the plains on our left.

On reaching the crest that overlooked a sharp-sided ravine called Acorn Hollow, we very soon spied the Indians a half-mile down the hollow, and perhaps a quarter of a mile north of us. They had evidently already discovered us, for they remained but a moment beside the stolen horse, which we found later they were in the act of repacking, and then they broke into a hasty retreat, leaving the animal behind.

They did not attempt to swing up into the hills, but instead pushed out across the high, open plain that extends northward toward Dry Creek. There were seven of them, Billy Sill being of the number. He was carrying a pair of my buckskin leggings across his arm.

Taking in the situation at a glance, Good remarked that he believed he could run down the hollow, follow the Indians out onto the open plain and overhaul them before they reached the shelter of Dry Creek, but I told him that I was going to hold my present position and try to head them from finally getting into Mill Creek.

Away then we went on our respective courses. I could see the Indians much of the time and could see Good many hundred yards behind them. His turning down the hollow added a half mile or more to his course, and the lead this gave the Indians was too much for him to overcome.

When the Indians scuttled into the brushy bottom of Dry Creek, he was still far out on the open plain. After leaving this depression, the redskins swerved to the right and sped up the long slope toward the breaks of Mill Creek. The many miles of the chase had left me by this time nearly blown. I saw that I was not going to be able to beat the Indians to the protecting belt of timber that lay on the crest of the slope. However, the courses we were now pursuing were bringing us gradually nearer together. I could see a dusky form now and then gliding upward through the trees and brush that sprinkled the hillside.

Putting forth a mighty effort, I increased my pace a trifle, and keeping this up for an eighth of a mile or so reached a spot from which I believed the scudding Indians must come into view. Almost immediately I saw the leader swing across the very space I had picked upon. He was considerably over two hundred yards away, but I knew that I was not going to get closer, so I threw up my rifle and fired at him. I missed, and he swiftly whirled about and returned the compliment. This gave me time for my second barrel, and he fell at the crack of my gun. The balance of the party glided like lightning behind covers and began pouring in a hot fire toward my place of concealment. Most of the their bullets flew high, as was invariably the case when the redskins were aiming downward. In fact, it was only now and then that a shot struck close to me. On the other hand, Good, who was far below me on the hillside, had a perfect shower of bullets dropping about him during the entire engagement. He was so completely exhausted by the long run across the plains that he did not get into the fight at all.

I kept pounding away as long as the Indians returned my fire, but so closely did they cling to their cover that I was not able to score a second time. After a time they worked back toward the top of the ridge, and, carrying off their wounded comrade, made good their escape into that everlasting haven of refuge,—the wilds of Mill Creek's Canyon.

Then I returned to Hi and we proceeded to help each other home. The tramp back across the plains was one of the hardest jobs I have ever undertaken. Words cannot express the relief we both felt when we at length reached the spot where the abandoned horse was awaiting us. One of my saddles had been cut to pieces to provide straps and strings for tying the stolen plunder onto the horse. This plunder consisted principally of corn and other vegetables which the Indians had collected from the gardens of Deer Creek.

We reached Hi's cabin late in the afternoon and were quite ready for our Sunday breakfasts. At the Carter place we found quite a party of neighbors collected. They had heard the firing and were just on the point of starting to our assistance.

A few weeks later a squaw coming from the hills reported that the wounded Indian had succumbed to his injuries, after a few days.

CHAPTER XII.

ONE day in June, 1863, Solomon Gore, who lived on Rock Creek, hurried to my house and reported that the Mill Creeks had stolen two horses from him. He asked me if I could get the animals back. I replied that I thought I could if I had someone to accompany me to the hills. Accordingly, Tom Gore and Jack Howser agreed to go with me.

We struck off northeasterly through the hills and were not long in finding the Indians' trail. I had no difficulty in following it, and we pushed forward rapidly. Shortly before night we met one of the stolen horses. It was a young animal, and had evidently escaped from the Indians in some way and was returning to its master.

We had started so late in the day that night overtook us before we had covered many miles. We made our beds by simply selecting convenient places to stretch our frames among the bowlders, where I, for one, slept tranquilly until morning.

With the break of day we were up and once more on the trail. We passed through the Singer Creek country and in a couple of hours came to the borders of the Deer Creek Flats.

As we approached the level land of the Flats, we spied five bears busily digging on an open space ahead. I knew that the Indians were many miles ahead of us, so I suggested to the boys that we have some fun with the bears.

"You may have all the fun you like," said Tom Gore, "but please wait until I get up a tree before you begin."

Jack Howser was of the same way of thinking. I laughed at them and told them to shin up their trees, but to leave a convenient one for me in case I should need it. They were not long in getting up into a couple of oaks, and then I moved cautiously out toward a large tree which enabled me, unseen, to approach within one hundred and fifty yards of the feeding bears. This tree was too large to be easily climbed, which was the reason I had selected a smaller one farther back.

The bears were totally unaware of our presence. I waited until the largest one turned full side toward me, when I raised my rifle and let her have it. She slashed at her ribs with her teeth and sent up a fierce bellow, but after a moment seemed to recover in a measure. At the very least, I had roused her curiosity, for she reared up and sat upon her haunches, looking extremely vicious. She was directly facing me, so I threw a second ball into her. Then she caught sight of me and charged. I ran for my tree and swung myself up into its branches. When I thought that I was out of the bear's reach, I looked back and was just in time to see her turn end for end as she ran. She did not rise and I afterward found that my second bullet had bitten off the end of her heart.

However, the other bears were yet to be reckoned with. They seemed to consist of two two-year-olds and two yearlings, probably all offspring of the old one. I reloaded my rifle, then dropped to the ground, Tom and Jack yelling at me as though they thought I was as good as eaten alive. One of the bears came a short distance toward me, and I sank on one knee, waited until it was within forty feet, then dropped it dead at one shot. The others were at a loss what to do. While they continued to sniff at the old one and to toddle about in perplexity, I killed two more of them and crippled the fifth one, which got away.

We secured the gall-bladders from the four dead animals, and then took up once more the trail of the Indians. I had little hopes of being able to overtake them short of Mill Creek Canyon, but, of course, I had to follow the trail in order to make sure.

We dropped down into Deer Creek and crossed this stream, as we had on several previous occasions, near the mouth of Sulphur Creek. Again the trail led us up that frightful ascent toward the wedge-like defile in the upper cliff, and, incredible as it may see, we found that the Indians had taken the stolen horse up that way. Tom and Jack declared that they could see scars upon the small trees where the animal had hung on by his teeth.

We crossed through the broad canyons of Little and Big Dry Creeks, and so at length reached the breaks of Mill Creek. From here we could see for miles over the wild regions of that great canyon, and I told the boys that we would take a good look before going farther, as there were ten chances to one that the Indians were snuggled away somewhere under our feet.

After a careful observation, I at length discovered some human figures moving about a hillside, fully two miles below us. We scrutinized them closely and came to the conclusion that it was a number of squaws, gathering grass-seed. Their camp was nowhere in sight, but I knew that we could find the camp by watching the squaws.

Bidding the boys to avoid being seen, as they would avoid a pestilence, I led them down the long slope, keeping as deeply as possible within the shelter of ravines and thickets. In this way we were enabled to approach within three hundred yards of the squaws.

We were lying under a jutting pile of rocks, peering out at them and picking out our next line of advance, when suddenly a signal shout was heard, coming from some point above us. I knew at once that we were discovered by a lookout. The squaws, however, paid no heed, evidently not having heard the cry; but in a moment it was repeated, and this time they heard it. In a moment they were scurrying down the hill.

"Our only show is to follow them!" I cried, and springing up I bounded down the hill in pursuit. I proved to be a swifter runner than my two comrades and soon left them behind. As I ran I heard one of them shoot, but I kept on, for I wanted to find the Indians' camp.

The fleeing squaws disappeared over a brow of the ridge, but I kept on down the point which led toward the creek, and all at once I came within full sight of the camp. It lay about two hundred yards below me and seemed to be in a state of confusion. I saw Indians flying about, trying to pile articles upon the single horse that stood in their midst. I could see that there were many bucks present, so waited a few moments for Tom and Jack to join me. They failed to put in an appearance, however, and I knew that I must act quickly or let the entire party escape. I watched for a good chance and soon, drawing down on a big fellow, added one more good Indian to the list with the first shot.

The other warriors immediately sprang to their guns and, locating me by the smoke from my rifle, began sending bullets whining and whistling about me. With the first volley they disappeared, dropping behind the rocks and bushes, but they continued to find the way to my position. For some time we exchanged shots. I was behind a tree which was not more than eight inches in diameter, though there were moments when I warmly wished that it were eight feet. However, having my double-barrel, I was able to fool them. They perceived that I was alone, and frequently, after I fired, some of them would expose themselves for a moment in seeking to secure better cover, and each time they made this mistake I dropped one in his tracks with my second barrel.

At length Jack and Tom came down to where I

lay, and a more helpless pair of Indian fighters I
never saw! One had the lock wrenched off his rifle,
while the other had his ramrod broken off in his gun-
barrel. Neither could fire a shot. At that time I had
my last bullet in my rifle, but luckily Tom's bullets
were the same calibre as mine. I quickly deprived
him of all he had, and just at that moment the Mill
Creeks turned loose a most vicious volley. The bullets plowed and hissed among the rocks beside us,
and in a second the two of them were trying to hide
with me behind my little eight-inch tree.

I told them that our only show was to charge and
put the Indians on the run. They agreed to follow
my lead, so we sprang out and rushed down the hill.
The Indians broke and fled and we gained their camp
in safety.

"Now hustle," said I, "or they will slip back and
make it hot for us from that brush!"

We soon had the recovered horse loaded with
such articles as we could hastily pick up. There
was a pile of new quilts lying beneath a tree, probably having been snatched from some foothill cabin,
and as I picked one of them up a lank Indian boy
sprang up and stood watching us in blank surprise.
He had slept peacefully through the entire battle.

"There's your chance!" said I to Tom and Jack.
"If you want to kill an Indian on this trip, bag that
fellow."

But neither of them would raise a hand against
him, and we went away and left him staring stupidly
after us.

When we reached the top of the ridge, we sat down for a breathing spell.

"Well, Bob," said Jack, "how many of those fellows do you think you got? I saw two."

"I counted three" said Tom.

I told them that I thought there were six or seven scattered along the hillside.

We struck off down the slope of the foothills and reached the valley without mishap. We went by way of Hi Good's cabin, and stopped there for lunch. Hi was at home and listened with great interest to an account of our experiences. He remarked, when we had finished:

"You fellows can consider that you got off very lucky. I came down through that country the other day, and took a peep at that camp, and there were at least thirty bucks there. I guess if the whole party had been at home that you three would have been left in the hills."

I told him that it looked to me like there were just about thirty warriors there when I opened fire upon them.

About two weeks later, Hi came one day to my place. He said that a squaw had come to his place from Mill Creek, a few days after we had paid our visit to the Indians' camp, and had told him that there were seven killed and two badly wounded in that battle, which proved that my estimate had not been far wrong.

CHAPTER XIII.

THE final conflict with the Mill Creeks occurred in 1865. I was then living at my present home, eight miles north of Chico. About the middle of August, business took me to the old grist mill that stood at the mouth of Butte Creek Canyon. I made the trip on horseback.

As I was riding up Edgar Slough, I noticed a group of some half a dozen men break from the woods at about the point where the Schwein slaughter-house now stands. On nearer approach, I perceived that they were all strangers. I also discovered that they were all armed and seemed to be in a state of great excitement.

"Have you seen a party of men anywhere on the road between here and Chico?" asked one, eagerly.

"How many?" I asked.

"Six."

"No. What's up?"

"We're after Bidwell's Indians!"

Then they told me how the Indians had made a raid into the Concow country, had killed a man and two women, horribly mutilating the latter, had slaughtered hogs and cattle out of pure cruelty, and had then melted away.

"Why do you think it the work of the Bidwell Indians?" I asked.

"We KNOW it is! Their trail leads straight out through the hills in this direction. We followed it to the Johnson place, and it points for Chico. Listen to that shooting, boys!"—for at that instant a shot or two and some cries were heard from toward Chico Creek. "Hurry up! let's don't miss it all!" and they were about to rush away.

"Gentlemen," said I, "you are barking up the wrong tree!"

They paused.

"What do you know about it?" asked one.

"Simply this: That trail you've been following is a blind. Bidwell's Indians haven't been near Concow, and Bidwell's Indians haven't killed anyone."

"Then what Indians did it?"

"The Mill Creeks."

They had all heard of the Mill Creeks, but some were still in doubt.

"Who are you?" asked one.

I told him my name, and they seemed more willing to listen to me. I assured them that the Bidwell Indians were perfectly quiet and well-behaved, and that the Mill Creeks had more than once attempted to saddle some of their own crimes upon them. I added that if they wished to find the real culprits they had better strike for the canyon of Deer Creek or of Mill Creek.

While we were talking, I saw a group of men leave the woods a mile or so east of us.

"There is the rest of your outfit," I said, and on approaching and joining them we found that this was true.

With this new party was one Bill Matthews; also a young man named Frank Curtis, who was a brother, I think, of Henry Curtis, who then conducted a tannery on Rock Creek, and with whom I was well acquainted.

I repeated what I had told the first-comers, and told them that they would surely breed trouble for themselves if they bothered Bidwell's Indians; and, besides, would be wasting their time and allowing the real culprits to escape.

A short consultation was held among their leaders, and then I was asked if I would lead them into the Mill Creek country. I replied that I had business at the grist mill, but that I would ride there and return as soon as possible, and would join them on Rock Creek. I assured them that there was not one chance in a hundred of our overtaking the Indians short of Mill Creek, and that there would be many miles of rough country to travel over before reaching that point.

I finished my mission at the mill, and, hurrying home, moved my family over to the Gore place on Rock Creek. The Concow men were awaiting me there, and we started next morning. Henry Curtis had joined the party and was practically leader of the Concow force.

I told Curtis that we would probably strike the trail on Deer Creek Flats, so we headed for that region. On Deer Creek we found Hi Good, who promptly joined us. We reached the Flats late in the afternoon, and there, sure enough, we found a fresh Indian trail leading toward the north.

We made camp beside the spring, on the Flats, and while gathered about the camp-fire before retiring it was suggested that we organize by electing a captain. I was elected and Good was chosen second in command.

Next morning we were up and away almost with the break of day. In order to make sure that the Indians had not dodged to right or left, I followed the trail, keeping usually about two hundred yards ahead of the main party, with Hi beside me as my lookout. In this way we filed down through the wild gorge of Deer Creek, across that stream, and on across the less rugged slopes of the two Dry Creeks, and so by the middle of the afternoon reached the top of the ridge which overlooks the broad canyon of Mill Creek.

Climbing to a point from which we had a good outlook, Good and I made a close inspection of the region below us. At length the glint as of some bright object caught my eye far down in the very bottom of the canyon. It was fully three miles distant. I believed it to be the sun flashing from a rifle-barrel and pointed it out to Hi. Soon we saw a tiny white object move down the side of a little rounded knoll close to the creek, and both recognized it as a human figure.

"That's their lookout," I said, "and I believe it's

Billy Sill. He had on a white shirt when he ran away. They are camped beside those three little knolls just the other side of the creek."

"Just this side, you mean," said Hi.

"No. The north side."

We both remembered the three knobs, but could not agree as to which side of the stream they occupied, and the water could not be seen from where we were to decide the matter. We argued for some time and at length Hi said:

"Well, you're the doctor. What shall we do?"

I replied that we would swing back around a high point on the summit of the ridge, march down to the bottom of the canyon, cross the creek a half mile or more below the three knolls, and then make our advance by moving up-stream.

This plan I communicated to the main party. We slipped into a hidden ravine and filed slowly and cautiously downward toward the bottom of the canyon, exercising the utmost care to keep from falling under the eye of the hawk-like lookouts that we knew were stationed on lofty points here and there. The ravine was very brushy and strewn with bowlders, yet at times we had to crawl on our hands and knees to remain hidden.

At last we accomplished the descent successfully, and waded through the foaming waters of Mill Creek to the north side. We were still a good, safe distance below where I knew the camp must be, so I ordered that the entire party advance slowly up-stream. We moved up some distance from the creek and kept under the coves that headed the glades.

A little before actual sunset,—the sun being gone long since from the bottom of that deep canyon,—a number of moving objects on the hillside below us caught my eye. I gave the signal to lie low, and the entire party sank down among the rocks.

Soon four squaws came filing along a dim trail, wending their way up the creek. We were not discovered, and the squaws passed on around a bend a few hundred yards above us and disappeared. This made Hi and I feel more certain than ever that the Indians were camped about in the region of the three knolls.

CHAPTER XIV.

I MOVED the party a short distance farther up-
stream, then grouped them beneath the spread-
ing branches of an oak and ordered them to lie
down and to remain absolutely quiet, until I should
return.

Selecting Good as my companion, we made plans
to find out, if possible, the exact location of the
camp. We removed our boots, laid aside our rifles,
and, with only our revolvers as weapons, slipped
into the water and started to make our way up-
stream. Our progress was extremely slow. The
night was very dark, and the stream was turbulent
and filled with bowlders. We tried to keep under
the bank as much as possible, for fear of brushing
into some sentinel above it, but at times found the
water too deep for us, when we were compelled to
crawl like snakes through the bordering fringe of
trees and brush.

Just below the three round-topped knolls the
stream broadened into a natural ford. The knolls
stood on the north side of the stream, and between
them and the ford lay a flat sand-bar. At length we
approached this broader stretch of water. The bank
broke off straight to the water. It was not over
three feet high and was clear of trees and brush.

Suddenly a dog broke forth into wild barking close in front of us, and, springing toward the bank, bayed furiously in our very faces. We could feel his hot breath and could have struck him with our six-shooters had we wished. Instead of turning about or making any attempt to beat a retreat, we crouched still for a minute or more, while the dog made the echoes of that deep canyon resound with his cries of defiance.

Peering over the bank in the midst of this uproar, we plainly perceived several forms rise up to sitting postures on the bar in front of us. We were almost abreast of the camp. The Indians probably thought that the dog was baying some wild beast, for none of them arose to investigate, and Good and I painstakingly made our way back down-stream, the dog following us to within one hundred yards of where the main party lay.

Just before we reached the point where we had entered the stream, Good, in some way, loosened a heavy stone from the bank, which rolled into the water, struck his bare foot and crushed off a toe-nail. I helped him bandage the injured member with a poultice of tobacco, after which we joined the rest of the party and made our plans for the attack upon the Indians.

We decided to move forward just in time to get the camp surrounded before the break of day. Hi, with six men, was left to advance upon the camp in the same manner that he and I had already adopted, while I took the balance of the force for a detour which would bring us against the Indians from the up-stream side.

We had a difficult climb, for we were compelled to swing some distance up the rough hillside in order to avoid springing an alarm, but made it successfully. As day began to peep over the high walls of the canyon, I found myself lying about thirty feet above one of the three little knolls that had served us so well as land-marks. I had left orders for Hi's party to lie quiet and let us make the attack. This would throw the Indians onto the bar next the open ford, where they would be completely at the mercy of both our forces.

It grew lighter and still no sound disturbed the morning excepting the incessant roar of the nearby stream. Henry Curtis was close to my right. Suddenly he chirped like a bird. I glanced toward him and saw him pointing toward the top of the knoll. Turning my eyes thither I was just in time to see the half-breed, Billy Sill, lowering his rifle in a line with my head. I rolled behind a tree, and the half-breed, knowing that he was seen, sank out of sight behind a rock. I had ample time, in the glimpse I caught of him, to see that he still wore a white shirt.

Almost on the instant that he disappeared, Good's rifle cracked, and the fight was on. We crowded forward and poured a hot fire into the Indians from up-stream, while Good's men hammered them from below. Into the stream they leaped, but few got out alive. Instead, many dead bodies floated down the rapid current.

Billy Sill made a break to escape by leaping straight up the mountain-side. Several shot at him, but missed. I swung my rifle on him and cut him down just as he was about to spring into a thicket. As he rolled toward the creek he cursed me venomously with his last breath. He was known to many of us, having lived from childhood with Uncle Dan Sill. He had been herding sheep for Sill a short time before this, when one day he left the band and joined the Mill Creeks.

This battle practically ended the scourge of the Mill Creeks. I had often argued with Good regarding the disposition of the Indians. He believed in killing every man or well-grown boy, but in leaving the women unmolested in their mountain retreats. It was plain to me that we must also get rid of the women. On this occasion the Concow people were intensely wrought up over the horrible atrocities practiced by the Indians on the white women whom they killed, and I had told them that they were at liberty to deal with the Indians as they saw fit.

While ransacking the camp after the battle was over, a little child possessing six toes on each foot was found. Hi Good at once took a notion to the child and said that he wished to take it home with him. Knowing that he had odd tastes about such things, I consented, whereupon he declared that he must take along a squaw to carry the child. I asked Curtis what his pleasure was in the matter, and, after consulting with some of his own party, he grudgingly agreed.

The woman selected for the purpose was slightly wounded in the heel. She packed the youngster in stolid silence up the long hill, and over its crest into Twenty-Mile Hollow. Here, however, she became sullen and refused to go a step farther. I gave her over to the Concow people and they left her to swell the number of the dead.

If I remember correctly, one of the women murdered by the Indians at Concow had recently come over from England and had in her possession several hundred dollars in English sovereigns. This money was taken by the murderers, but we failed to find any of it.

However, at this time Sandy Young was stopping at Big Meadows, in charge of the Bidwell stock. The marauding Mill Creeks, in the course of their raid, had swung around by the Meadows, where they had killed a number of the Indians of that region and carried away a number of squaws.

The Big Meadows red-men were afraid of their desperate enemies, and would not take the field against them except under Young's leadership. Consequently, the latter got a force together and came down through Deer Creek Meadows and Onion Creek and so along the Lassen Trail to Bluff Camp, where they swung into Mill Creek Canyon.

They reached the old camp at the three knolls just three days after we had been there. Sandy said that it looked as though a cyclone had struck that spot. In making a search over the battle-ground he found where something had been buried in the sand

and a fire made above it to hide the spot. Examiinng
it closely, he unearthed an English sovereign. The
balance of the money had evidently been dug up and
carried away by the survivors among the Indians,
and probably today lies hidden away in some one of
the many caverns of that mighty canyon.

CHAPTER XV.

IT was well known that several bucks and a number of squaws and children escaped during that last fight at the three knolls. They remained hidden away in the depth of the canyons, sallying out occasionally to plunder foothill cabins, but dealing no more death to the white man. Their reign of mischief-making seemed to be at an end, and yet were they to be heard from, at least indirectly, once more.

After many months a number of squaws humbly presented themselves to Hi Good and told him that the entire remnant of the tribe would surrender if assured of his protection. Hi was then living on Dry Creek. Negotiations were carried on for some time, and at length two bucks and three squaws, with a number of children, moved down to Good's place and told him that they were ready to be taken to the Reservation.

However, reduced as they were to this pitiful handful, their innate treachery had not been beaten out of them. Living with Good was an Indian boy whom he had raised from childhood. This boy was now about sixteen, and I have never had a doubt that he was influenced by the older Indians to turn traitor against the man who had given him a home.

With genuine Indian patience he watched and

waited for his opportunity. It came one day when
Good rode over to the Carter place on Deer Creek
for vegetables. After he was gone, the Indian boy
took Hi's rifle and slipped after him. He met Good
returning near Acorn Hollow, a brush-sided ravine
that puts out from the hills less than a mile north of
Deer Creek.

Hi was walking and leading his horse by means of
the bridle-rein, the animal carrying a sack of garden
stuff. The Indian permitted his victim to get within
easy range, when, from his hidden lair, he took deliberate aim and fired. Good fell, but rose again and
started toward his assailant. The Indian, being un-
injured, easily kept out of his grasp, and a second
and a third bullet he drove into the white man's
body before the latter sank down dead.

The murderer then tried to dispose of the body.
He placed a rope around the dead man, and, looping
it to the saddle-horn, dragged the body some distance up the hollow, rolled it over a step bank, then,
climbing down, piled stones upon it.

The older Indians at once fled to the hills, but
the boy, if he went with them, soon returned to Dry
Creek. Inquiries for Good were soon made and the
conduct of the Indian boy excited suspicion. He
had an unusual amount of money in his possession,
and was found to be wearing a large silver ring of
Hi's upon his finger. Furthermore, he boastfully
carried Hi's rifle about with him.

Friends instituted a search and the body was
soon found. The Indian boy was taken to Acorn

Hollow by Sandy Young and a number of others. When shown the dead body, he at first denied all knowledge of the crime; but soon his manner altered and he calmly made a full confession, and even led the whites to the spot where the fatal shots had been fired, and explained every step of the tragedy.

After all had been told, Sandy significantly picked up his rifle, and his companions slipped away, knowing that an act of retributive justice was about to be enacted. Soon the sharp crack of the rifle rang out above the chaparral and the last chapter in the tragic death of Hi Good had been written.

A word as to the other members of our party who trailed and fought the Indians through so many hard days. Breckenridge went to the lower country, where he met his death in a campaign against the Indians of Arizona. Simmons, Martin and Williams drifted to other regions, where I lost all trace of them. "Bully" went to Nevada, where he secured employment as hunter for a force of soldiers. While so employed, he one day met a group of Piute Indians. They exchanged cordial greetings as they rode past, but after riding a few rods they suddenly whirled and shot him in the back, killing him instantly.

Sandy Young lived in Chico for a number of years after most of the others had passed away. Finally, in company with Dan Sutherland, he went to the Klamath River and engaged in mining. There he mysteriously disappeared. His body was never found, but it is generally believed that he was